Awake in the River

# AWAKE IN THE RIVER

*Poetry/Prose by*
*Janice Mirikitani*

Isthmus Press / 1978

Some of these works have appeared in :
*Time to Greeze!, Third World Women, Bridge
Magazine, Counterpoint, Aion, Asian American
Heritage, Rikka* ("... I Still Carry It Around,"
an essay by Hisaye Yamamoto), *Odes to Bill
Sorro, Mark in Time, Ayumi,* and others.

cover design : Chester Yoshida
center graphic : Gail Aratani
photo : Nancy Wong

First Edition 1978
Second Edition 1982
Third Printing 1984

. . . .
And yet,
     we were not devoured
     we were not humbled
     we are not broken.

## For My Father

He came over the ocean
carrying Mt. Fuji
on his back/Tule Lake on his chest
hacked through the brush
of deserts
and made them grow
strawberries

       we stole berries
       from the stem
       we could not afford them
       for breakfast

his eyes held
nothing
as he whipped us
for stealing.

the desert had dried
his soul.

wordless
he sold
the rich,
full berries
to hakujines
whose children
pointed at our eyes

       they ate fresh
       strawberries
       with cream.

Father,
I wanted to scream
at your silence.
Your strength
was a stranger
I could never touch.

iron
in your eyes
to shield
the pain
to shield desert-like wind
from patches
of strawberries
grown
from
tears.

# Sing With Your Body

*for my daughter, Tianne Tsukiko*


We love with great difficulty
spinning in one place
afraid to create
                    spaces
                            new rhythm

the beat of a child
dangled by her own inner ear
takes Aretha with her

                    upstairs,   somewhere
go quickly, Tskuiko,

                    into your circled dance
go quickly

                    before your steps are
                    halted by who you are not

go quickly

                    to learn the mixed
                    sounds of your tongue,

go quickly

                    to who you are

                    before

                            your mother swallows
                            what she has lost.

## *August 6*


Yesterday
a thousand cranes
were flying.
Hiroshima,
your children
still dying

   and they said

   it saved many lives

the great white heat
that shook flesh from bone
melted bone
to dust

   and they said
   it was merciful

yesterday
a thousand cranes
were flying.
Obachan
offered omame
to her radiant Buddha
incense smoking miniature
mushrooms
her lips moving
in prayer
for sister they found
tatooed to the ground
a fleshless shadow on Hiroshima soil

   and they said
   Nagaski

Yesterday
a woman
bore a child
with fingers
growing from her neck
shoulder
empty

                    and they said
                    the arms race

Today
a thousand cranes
are flying
and in expensive waiting rooms
of Hiroshima, California
are blood counts
sucked by the white death

                    and they said
                    it might happen again

tonight
while
everyone sleeps
memoryless
the night wind
flutters like a thousand wings
how many ears will hear
the whisper
"Hiroshima"
from a child's
armless shoulder
puckered
like a kiss ?

## Loving from Vietnam to Zimbabwe

Here in this crimson
room
with silk skimming our skin
I shape into thought
these strange burnings
starting in my fingertips
as they lick your nipples,
hairs standing to the touch.

> You are marching in
> the delta
> the river water
> at your boots
> sucking through the leather
> sand has caked your color yellow.

Your chest moves
to the rhythm of my heart
warm skin singing

> you plod weighted by
> days of marching
> nights of terror
> holding this patch of ground
> shaped like a crotch.

my teeth on your
shoulder
hungry to enter your flesh
as you call me strange names.

> water/water
> sinking sand
> they are coming
> as your raise the blade
> of your bayonet
> clean it with
> your sweat.

My mouth driven
to your thighs
the sweet inside
just below the swinging
songs of your life.

       Deeper into
       the mekong
       the grass has eyes
       the wind has flesh
       and you feel the trigger
       pressed back for release

your thighs tremble
your long fingers like marsh grass
in my hair
as i reach down
onto Mt. Inyangani

       you have seen them
       hanging in the trees
       after american troops
       had finished/
       slanted eyes bugging
       crooked necks
       genitals swinging from
       their mouths.

Sweat from your neck
I think they are tears
as i move
into the grassy plain
of your chest.

       You never saw them
       but knew they looked like me
       and you got sick a lot
       wondering what color
       their blood.

As I hold
your skin between my
teeth
I can feel the blood
pulsing
on my tongue
spurting like the
beginning of
Zambezi    River.

                You turned in your rage
                knowing how they have used you.
                Not the invisible ones
                whose soil you were sent to seize
                but those behind you
                pushing you
                pulling
                pulling
                your trigger.

And I massage
your back
large/black like the shadowed
belly of a leaf
as you in
your stillness
hold me like
a bird.

                they stripped you
                held you down
                in the sand
                took the bayonet off your gun
                and began to slice
                lopped off your head
                and expected you to die.

I, in the
heavy hot air
between us,
in the crimson room
that begins to blur
feel you enter
my harbor/kiss the lips
of my soul

## Call me Strange Names

> hanoi
> bachmai
> haiphong

loving in this world
is the sliver splinting
edge
is the dare
in the teeth of the tiger
the pain of jungle rot
the horror of flesh unsealed
the danger of surviving.

## Desert Flowers

Flowers
faded
in the desert wind.
No flowers grow
where dust winds blow
and rain is like
a dry heave moan.

Mama, did you dream about that
beau who would take you
away from it all,
who would show you
in his '41 ford
and tell you how soft
your hands
like the silk kimono
you folded for the wedding?
Make you forget
about That place,
the back bending
wind that fell like a wall,
drowned all your geraniums
and flooded the shed
where you tried to sleep
away hyenas?
And mama,
bending in the candlelight,
after lights out in barracks,
an ageless shadow
grows victory flowers
made from crepe paper,
shaping those petals
like the tears
your eyes bled.
Your fingers
knotted at knuckles
wounded, winding around wire stems
the tiny, sloganed banner:

"america for americans".

                              Did you dream
                              of the shiny ford
                              (only always a dream)
                              ride your youth
                              like the wind
                              in the headless night ?

Flowers
2¢ a dozen,
flowers for American Legions
worn like a badge
on america's lapel
made in post-concentration camps
by candlelight.
Flowers
watered
by the spit
of "no japs wanted here",
planted in poverty
of postwar relocations,
plucked by
victory's veterans.

                              Mama, do you dream
                              of the wall of wind
                              that falls
                              on your limbless desert,
                              on stems
                              brimming with petals/crushed
                              crepepaper
                              growing
                              from the crippled
                              mouth of your hand ?

Your tears, mama,
have nourished us.
Your children
like pollen
scatter in the wind.

# Watergate, U.S.

"The deadliest evil is when 'recognized'
power works against the good of all people . . ."

Cecil Williams

It is a time like no other.

    In the streets

    the children

    play with dogs

    who have smelled

    the danger of sleepless giants

    frightened and dying

    fucking their bitches

    in fantasies of

    young men.

The heat is unbearable.
Dried, white heat
sweating with peoples' hunger

It is a time like no other

    The dried, white dying giants

    walk their women

    who suck the erect heat

    of air

    led by the leash of unfulfilled

    promises

    splaying their smell

    for hot, young men

    held hungry,

    hopeless.

It is a time like no other

the woman
dangled like meat
on a spear
by dried white dying giants
who lie about their love for women
their hate for themselves.

It is a time like no other

When cannibals
and giants
battle
for the smell of the woman
and the giants' limbs
torn, rent
leaving only his member
dangled on a spear.

The woman eats it

gags
gives up her mind
clothes her body
with her smell
for bait
while the hot
young men
wait
hopeful
hungry
to become giants.

## The First Generation

Elegy to my grandmother

Bent and knotted as a wintered vine
she watched her daughters grow from her
in a hybrid land
and the grandchildren thick around
no longer her own.

Hototogisu naki naki
*(The cuckoo cries cries*

She grew wisteria
as a temple
in her garden
and there kept her private peace

Oto hitori ame de ato
*the only sound after rain*

The children mocked the old ways
shook the fragile vines in their play
while silently she made a wreath
of the dying blossoms

shizuka no jimen arau
*washes the land with quiet)*

Her love wore long
as my sorrow.
The withered roots
have given back beauty to the soil.

# Japs

(Inspired by a play by Hiroshi Kashiwagi
"Plums Can Wait" about migrant Japanese
American farmers after WWII)

Owls with open mouths
watch mutely
as rapists come
and ravage the plums
hanging heavy
like a waiting woman's breast.
They will soften
before the boxes are built.
The slant eyed midget
works harder
sweats more
as the boss's wife
watches from her shaded window
the short arms
lugging long planks,
nails
protruding from his palms.
She wanted to hate him, who
never spoke
planeing the wood
nailing them tightly together
like thighs.
Owls with open mouths
watch
as the rapists
lurk behind
shaded windows
wondering at midgets
quickening among the plums,
moving faster
strides shorter,
and the plums
like ripe breasts
always above his reach.

She felt
rage at the slant eyed
short armed
quick moving
midget/the jap
who made her
watch the walls at night
when sleepless
the owls called.
The boss would not
let him go
he worked too well.
And the wife
chipping the midget
like a knife,
her words/hate
as she tried to make
him/weaker/anything
and he would
bend/silently/packing boxes
with full/soft plums.
Owls with open mouths
see the rapist
offer the midget
a 5¢ raise in pay/a day
if he will fuck
the wife.
The midget jap
pins the long planks
with nails
from his hands
making boxes
as the wife rapist
lurks behind the window shade
while flies collide
over the dead owl,
eyes staring
haunts her.

if you're too dark
they will kill you.
if you're too swift
they will cripple you.
if you're too strong
they will buy you.
if you're too beautiful
they will rape you.

Watch with eyes open
speak darkly
turn your head like the owl
behind you.
They are coming
to nail you to boxes.

# A Certain Kind of Madness

After the assassination of
Orlando Letelier of Chile &
Steve Biko of South Africa

Incense
white paper
Somber kimono sleeves
lapping at the coffin.
Water spilling
from each face,
burying auntie.
My mother is there
trying to hide me.
The smell of dead bodies
makes my mind
pain.
It's my form of madness.

After the war,
auntie would cry
at night
tried to bury her face in the mattress
so we wouldn't hear.
And they would whisper
about her forgetfulness
her thinness
and trembling that would not stop.
In frozen silence
the black shoes gather
at the incense cup.
Momma, you wonder why I don't speak
anymore.
The smell of dead bodies
makes my mind pain
It's my form of madness

When we saw Letelier blown up
in a car, front screen
you said he must've done something bad.

I told you
there are hunters who kill by color :

 the gold tinted flesh
 that shines in its sweat
 rice eating creatures
 who plant in the sea.
 brown backed bodies
 blended to earth
 that once ran free
 in mountains behind Managua.
 black glistening
 shoulders moving to
 wind sobs, in the
 streets of Soweto.

There are those
who are hunted and killed for pleasure.

 When Biko went
 they thought silence would
 follow
 like rows of white stones.

What form of madness ?

Did auntie
eat the sandwich
left on the road for ants ?
You said
hunger is not a question
it is a disgrace.
Don't speak of it.

You are mad, you said
when I asked you
about the train
we boarded years ago
for those cages in the desert.
Didn't you know
they were smiling/ṣmiling
while you
thrashed like a rabbit
entangled in barbed wire.

Momma, did we do something bad ?

There are hunters who kill beauty
for pleasure
to fill their coffers
from the sale of your flesh
who kill free moving things
to stop them from hurting their eyes.

The smell of dead bodies
It's my form of madness.
But I tell you

These words I do speak
I don't do well in a cage.
It's lonely there.
I won't dwell in a cage
It's my form of madness.

## Jungle Rot and Open Arms

for a Vietnam Veteran brother, ex-prisoner

Leavenworth
and jungle rot
brought him
back to us
brimming with hate
and disbelief
in love or
sympathy.

his johnnywalker red
eyes
tore at my words
shred my flesh
made naked my
emptiness.

my anger
for the enemy heads
of state
boiled to nothing
            nothing
in the wake
of his rage

jungle rot
had sucked his bones,
his skin fell
like the monsoon
his brain
in a cast in Leavenworth.

In the midst
of genocide
he fell in love
in Vietnam.

                    "Her hair was
                       long and dark – like yours"
                              he said
                    "her eyes held the
                       sixth moon
                       and when she smiled
                       the sky opened
                       and I fell through.

I would crawl
in the tall grasses
to her village

and sleep the war
away with her
like a child on my thighs

I did not know
of the raid

and woke

with her arm
still clasping mine

I could not find
the rest of her

so I buried her arm
and marked my grave."

We sat in a silence
that mocks fools
that lifts us to the final language.

his breath sapped by B-52's
his eyes blinded by the blood of children
his hands bound to bayonets
his soul buried in a shallow grave

i stood amidst
his wreckage
and wept for myself.

so where is my
*political education* ? my
*rhetoric answers* to everything ? my
*theory into practice* ? my
*intensification of life in art* ?

words
are
like
the stone,
the gravemarker
over an arm
in Vietnam.

## Salad

The woman
did not mean to
offend me,

her blue eyes
blinking
at the glint
of my blade,

as I cut
precisely
like magic
the cucumber in
exact, even,
quick slices.

Do you orientals
do everything
so neatly ?

## Ms.

I got into a thing
with someone
because I called her
miss ann/hearst/rockerfeller/hughes
instead of ms.

I said
it was a waste of time
worrying about it.

Her lips pressed white
thinning words like pins
pricking me – a victim of sexism.

I wanted to
call her what
she deserved
but knowing it would please her
instead
I said,

> white lace & satin was never soiled by
> sexism
> sheltered as you are by mansions
> built on Indian land
>
> your diamonds shipped with slaves from Africa
> your underwear washed by Chinese launderies
> your house cleaned by my grandmother

so do not push me any further.

And when you quit
killing us
for democracy
and stop calling ME *gook*.

I will call you
whatever you like.

I HATE YOU
WOMAN

YOU IN YOUR SMALL MIND
SQUEEZING INSECURITIES
GRAPLING AFTER GOSSIP MINDED
BOURGEOIS BIGOTS

I HATE YOU
WOMAN

YOUR FUMBLING MISINTERPRETATIONS
CONTROLLING LIVES
THAT ARE NOT YOURS
BECAUSE YOU CANNOT LIVE FOR YOURSELF

I HATE YOU
WOMAN

YOUR MANIPULATION
GUILT CREATING – PUTTING INTO BOXES
EVERYTHING YOU DON'T WANT TO
UNDERSTAND. DON'T GIVE ME THIS SHIT.

I HATE YOU
WOMAN

BECAUSE YOU CANNOT
KEEP YOUR MAN
YOU ONLY CAN NAG HIM
INTO SUBMISSION

I HATE YOU
WOMAN

FOR IMPOSING YOUR LIFE
IN MINE
FOR STEALING MY ENERGY
AND TIME
FOR BEING IN MY MIND

I HATE YOU
WOMAN

        FOR YOUR LIES
        TO YOURSELF
        FOR THE SMALL CAUSES
        YOU UNDERTAKE TO
        LIMIT YOUR EGO

I HATE YOU
WOMAN

        FOR YOUR COLD
        MISCOMPREHENSION
        YOUR SELF PITY
        AND DECEPTION
        YOUR MINDLESS CONTRACEPTION
        AGAINST LIFE

I HATE YOU
WOMAN

        YOU

                WHO ARE

                        MIRRORED

                                IN ME.

## Bitches Don't Wait

Stayed up
half the night
wondering
knowing
where are you
it's better
to have
more than one
it makes you
anxious to come back
to me when you're thru.
Bitches don't wait.
don't play those games
sleeping around
with fools
who don't care
about my fine
sensitive woman nature.
i'd rather
stand on the corner
in my short
slit chong sam
or my wide necked
kimono
massaging
muscles for a dime
in some anonymous
room
warm, moist,
and smelling like
that opening
from where we all come
the room
like a wide screaming
mouth
melting coconut oil
on you
after a steaming bath
your bodies dripping
like my eyes
we won't get bored
'cause i won't even know you.

my virginal soul
will wait
and wait
for you.
keeping the bed
like an altar
wrap the sheets
on your feet
finger your hem
and you will always
return.
Does it hurt
because i know you are
with the one you're with
and you do your love thing
as i wait here
not present to you ?
It hurts
'cause i would
rather write a better line
stroke poems
like antelope
feel the Miles
blues like warm
honey
capture tigers
in China
and sleep in the folds
of their great breathing shanks.
i will go now to my street
when the work is done
coat my skin
with a violet gown
haloed with hood
oils in my hands
water
in my vessel
a net in
my thighs
and i will
sell
my body for a dime

                       while i don't wait
                       for you.

# The Winner

Aunt Sumi was a shadow with poorly fitted teeth. I remember her smile because the rest of her face was hidden by long surviving bruises.

>Tets would come home
>yell about the Chinamen
>who hung around the shed
>out back, playing ma jong
>after they had done their work.

Sumi cringed around corners, listening to a little joy, snatching the virile movement of arms swinging down tiles.

After her illness, I was sent to help clean her house. She seemed unable to organize herself, not knowing what to do next. The dishes would begin to smell from 3 day fish and hamu, still sticking on the tin.

She never heard me as I complained about the hard work made harder by her neglect. She would smile and tell me how much I had grown since the last time she had seen me, a week ago.

>O, the men
>will be after you
>soon enough.
>You can have your pick
>if you're careful.
>Perfect/You've got to be
>perfect.

Her words bleeding off my back, as I dusted and swept.

>He used to be a good man
>bring me flowers
>Take me
>to the races
>and show me
>a fine time
>Let me bet
>a couple of dollars
>on the high stepping one
>with a white star
>on her head
>And I would wear
>my dress with the roses on it
>and my white shoes
>And he would laugh a lot
>when I jumped up and down
>screaming the Star in
>on a win.

She knew the two worlds well. Being what she dreamed. Dreaming what she was not. She would tell me to be restrained. To be refined and dignified. Not to talk a lot and say the wrong things. Not to to smile too much. Only in silence will men imagine perfection.

> But Tets
> would tell me he loved
> my teeth.
> They were white and well shaped
> and they lit up my face when
> I talked.

And she told me to be good. In everything. If you're graceful they will woo you forever. If you are quiet, they will want to marry you. If you are obedient, you will remind them of their mother. You must never show them that you are smart. Or that you long for anything else except the world they can give you.

> Star knew she was
> the best.
> Her lovely head high
> at the starting gate,
> her step sassy with pride
> When she ran
> my breath would stop.
> She was so free.
> And she was a winner
> I could tell.
> The jockey would never have
> to use the whip on her.
> I told Tets
> they never whip a winner.

I would stop and look at Sumi's face. It was almost beautiful in the light, talking about Tets back then, her love for the courage of that horse. Her skin translucent through the bruises. Her eyes took on a shine that was not in this world. Her forehead was smooth with happiness and her lips were full, spilling those memories.

Outside we could hear the men laughing. Someone had won. Looey and his friends from other farms. Looey spoke little English when he came to this country. Tets and Sumi took him in. Tets did not like him at all.

> Chinamen
> all alike
> rather gamble
> and sleep
> than work.

Looey was a practical solution to their hardships when they returned from the camps. The farm did not yield enough for profit, and Looey was free labor in exchange for a place to stay. Tets took on work other places, fixing cars and doing carpentry for hakujines.

I don't know when the beatings began. I overheard momma say that after the war, when times were so bad, Tets would get drunk a lot and stay away. Sumi, who could never keep her mouth shut, would nag him, and she'd come over wearing dark glasses because her eyes were so swollen and black. It was like that for years.

Dusting the glass cases that held fine dolls from Japan, one dressed in a purple kimono with gold woven onto the obi, with white cranes embroidered on its sleeve, faced porcelained white, Sumi would follow my movements, jumping in time.

> The doll from Japan
> his mother sent
> before the war
> We gave it to the Johanssens
> to keep for us
> when we went into camp,
> and Tets into the army.
> I was so proud
> of him in uniform.
> He was handsome
> And before he left
> he was very kind to me.

Her eyes wandered far. I wondered if she was silent in their lovemaking. She merged time.

> Tets and I
> once
> when love flowed,
> we, in stride as one.
> It was a feeling
> like watching Star
> run
> against the wind
> muscles rubbing
> other horses
> as she passed
> her neck stretching
> to make her legs
> reach farther
> And for a moment
> with all flesh straining
> with nostrils
> enlarging to suck more breath
> I thought my heart would burst.

Breaking the memory, she moved to the kitchen. Too young . . . she mumbled, started a task, stopped, began to wander again.

> The last time
> I saw him
> I thought I was finished.
> He used his fists
> broke a lot of dishes
> that doll too.
> Looey tried to stop him
> but he was bleeding
> and dazed.
> Tets had the strength
> of madness
> I blacked out, came to
> with him straddling me
> my dress wet
> his fists in my belly
> I couldn't move
> with him sitting on me like that
> my mouth full
> of teeth rattling
> and my hair was
> scattered around me on the floor.
> I knew I was going to die
> His eyes told me
> His eyes, fixed, dark, foreign
> while his arms
> kept coming down
> whipping the sides of my face.

Sumi had been in the hospital, not waking for three days. Tets had left, and we never saw him again. They kept her for weeks. Testing, probing, useless treatments. She was not the same.

She married Looey. He was gentle, patient with her illness, her toothless clucking. The family was upset for a long time. People were talking too much. Obachan's heart broke and Ojichan would not permit her name to be uttered in his house again. Momma said that Tets had come home and found Sumi and the Chinaman in bed.

> Those were some days
> Tets laughing
> as I stood on the railing
> near home stretch
> That horse coming around the bend
> like an army

my legs
pumping Star in
jumping for her freedom
from the other horses trying to
block her/capture her
as she sucked in the wind.
And me,
leaping to the finish line
screaming for the
winner.

## Looking for a Poem

. . . What's Pablo up to? I'm here. If you
look for me in the street, you'll find me there
tuning my fiddle, ready to sing and to die . . .*
            *Pablo Neruda*

I wander
thru the rubble
of images cast aside

          rain, swelling from old wood,
          a house smelling of generations
          now asleep,
          fish in ancient dance for our birth,
          a broken hoe,
          pickled vegetables,
          fire of war/empty eyes/
          charred bones.

The poem
lies here somewhere
as easy as a human kiss
but when I'm asked
why not a love poem,
anger is easier.
Frantic,
I search until too tired.
Retreat to his words
and he shouts :

     "Look for me in the street(s).
        You'll find me there . . . ready to sing or to die . . ."

Search the earth.
Some of us never stretch the circumference
Neruda flew around the world
like light, and still had time
to dance with lions,
speak wisdom to the sun,
admire the legs of women,
leap fences with children and antelope,
plant songs in the trenches of Santiago,

*Quoted from "For Everybody", by Pablo Neruda
*Five Decades : Poems 1925-1970*, Grove Press, Inc. (New York, 1974)

His words

> like the stride of strong thighs
> the nostrils of horses mating
> the blood of women bearing
> the shoulders of soldiers embattled
> the hands of a fiddler, singing

Don't ask
where is the love poem

> Look . . . he is in the streets
> "ready to sing or to die."

# We, the Dangerous

I swore
it would not devour me
I swore
it would not humble me
I swore
it would not break me.

    And they commanded we dwell in the desert
    Our children be spawn of barbed wire and barracks

We, closer to the earth,
squat, short thighed,
knowing the dust better.

    And they would have us make the garden
    Rake the grass to soothe their feet

We, akin to the jungle,
plotting with the snake,
tails shedding in civilized America.

    And they would have us skin their fish
    deft hands like blades / sliding back flesh / bloodless

We, who awake in the river
Ocean's child
Whale eater.

    And they would have us strange scented women,
    Round shouldered / strong and yellow / like the moon
    to pull the thread to the cloth
    to loosen their backs massaged in myth

We, who fill the secret bed,
the sweat shops
the launderies.

    And they would dress us in napalm,
    Skin shred to clothe the earth,
    Bodies filling pock marked fields.
    Dead fish bloating our harbors.

We, the dangerous,
Dwelling in the ocean.
Akin to the jungle.
Close to the earth.

    Hiroshima
    Vietnam
    Tule Lake

And yet we were not devoured.
And yet we were not humbled
And yet we are not broken.

# Spoils of War
## (excerpt)

She could barely breathe, the desire was so heavy, like the weight of a wave, wafting her around in a vast sea. He was very blond, very blue and very sure of himself. Their lovemaking was wet, heaving. His weight on her pressed her deep into a place she thought she had dreamed about a long time ago.

The grasses grew high during the early spring. Lupins, deep purple, swung by the wind like a wave of dancers. The smell was so sweet, she thought she could pluck and eat. The color deep like pools in sleeves of stored kimonoes. She wove the full stems into a wreath. "Don't wear live flowers, or there will be death in the family," her mother warned.

She would slip them into the throat of her grandmother's lap, as she rocked in her silent timelessness. Grandma, always rocking, as if to nurse memories of another place. The family all vied and competed for her – she was magic, glowing from her quiet secret of peace. When grandma died, she felt a deep guilt.

The men were a silent, commanding presence . . . wordless except for spurts of hostility and occasional glowing threats of violence. Perhaps because of the inflexible will of these men, bound tightly within, giving nothing of their deep selves for the women to nurture, that the women had little to reflect themselves. The cycle perpetuated was isolation / surface blank mirrors / unspoken seethings.

What she knew best was the steady, controlled progression to survive, like the turning of a slow wheel.

She longed for the intensity of verbal presence . . . but he tried to maneuver her into the bed. His impatient need, the words to get more, get more.

The distance he created after it was over drove her to perform strange soundings : turmoil, dependency, exotic addition. She didn't even know how she did it, turning on her side, weeping. Telling him of the deep hurt he would inflict. And he would appease, weakly.

What he represented . . . a power only they possessed . . . that they could turn minds into libraries, laboratories, brick buildings, bombs. Somewhere in the back of her being she was awed. They could demolish an entire people and no one questioned their supreme authority to do so. The people, whom she knew in her mind, and had been able to feel the edges of their reality through grandparents, were somehow mystically related to sea creatures. She saw how when they became dangerous, they were destroyed. But still, Japan was just a name. Like "parent". Like "camps". Like "Issei, Nisei, Sansei, Yonsei."

Birth by Fire.

"Burn it." Yuki said, eyes flowing like spigots. Hard wet eyes, determined to see the red silk wrapping the emblem, the dense character filled, folded scrolls for the last time. Destroy by fire. "So they don't find any trace of home here. Burn it." The fire lept and swallowed paper, silk, even porcelain. Flames yellowed as the last strand melted. That day, only the sounds of fire's final licking, the dying, sucked the densely quiet room. Yuki's womb still draining hot afterbirth.

Bundles, knotted tightly, quickly, some left behind, heavy like the bodies lifting them to the truck taking them to the depot. Signs, posted on the door, flapped like an obscene wing, waving farewell:

"instructions to all persons of Japanese ancestry persuant to the provisions of Civilian Exclusion Order No. 33, dated April 22, 1942, all persons of Japanese ancestry both alien and non alien will be evacuated . . ."

Yuki, her bundles, boarded the train, infant in arms. Sachiko, her eight year old niece, trailed behind her, pulling her coat, a tag like those used to mark luggage, tied around her neck. Eyes cold. No longer flowing, lips pressed as the infant writhed in hunger, tightly screaming, Yuki sat. "Burn it," she whispered as the train steamed to start. Bodies, familiar . . . Sachiko, Okasan, Otosan, limply rocked like the bundles in the motion of the train. Silent weeping whispered to the rhythm of its wheels. Sachiko was gagging.

She flopped properly when Gerald fucked her, pressing her deep within herself, until she was transformed into that which his weight would define. She didn't think she cared about climax, only that he thought she had it. She was caught somewhere between the spoken complaint and the need to be opaque. Others had told her and Gerald repeated: you are not inadequate because of anything the others say, but because you are. You make it so, inherently.

Yuki watched out the window. Another time, though time blurred like the trees, hills, specks of animals the train left behind. Chicago to California. California to Tule Lake.

Her child, now five, crumpled next to her, bag over her mouth, gagging steadily from motion sickness all the way from Illinois to Utah. Her new husband slept across from her, mouth open in his snoring. He was no comfort. Already in their short time of marriage he began to change, now openly cruel to the child. She was dazed at his apparent hatred toward it. Because it was ugly – "Look, those eyes, puffed up folds. Teeth rolling out."

She felt the desert in her bones. And it frightened her so she clung to him to hide the dread, the darkening yawn of emptiness. She thought it would be better if they moved to California. It would be alright now since the war was over for a few years. They wouldn't be so cruel to them, as memory and hatred grew dimmer. He would be able to feel freer, perhaps his pride less hurt on the farm, relatively independent. It's better to owe her parents than be owned by a company, they rationalized.

How long ago, this same feeling. The train, and this desolation. This child, an infant in my arms. Sachiko next to me, gagging. Swallow the vomit. There are so many people. Shame on shame. Sickness, the smell, the red swollen faces from so much crying. Rigid resignation. Trees fading, wind and sand blowing. Sage scattered like skeletons. Clouds like ghosts mocking in the dry, dry, heat.

She didn't have the strength to be sympathetic anymore. The child would mercifully sleep for several hours, wake up gagging over her mother's skirt. How much more can she get up ? No food for days. She was getting so weak, flopping like a cloth over her mother's lap. They both hung in the motion of the train, speeding through the endless flats of salt.

How familiar, my skin feeling the airless wind. The smell of vomit all around me. Then the barracks spiking the ground. Wondering what the crime. My infant, wet, weak from the journey. Rash breaking from her face. A rush to the crudely constructed toilets. Guards looking through us. And the stall-less places. Strangers looking on my crouching nakedness. Red humiliation cloaking me. The smell of naked piss.

Don't you think it wrong to be so pompous ? Cold ? Critical ? Keeping me isolated ? Weakened by guilt. Her feeble attempts to define herself were unheard, perhaps because they were mouthed with little resolve. The weakness was reinforced somehow by the ever opening of her thighs, the hungry tight closing around him as he pressed her deeply into the bed.

As long as she could remember, she did not exist. There was physical body, thin legs and arms, small torso, flat hips, and a face that changed as often as the reactions to it. There was a thing they did praise . . . the length and shape of her thighs. Otherwise, she was flat, faceless.

She remembered the childhood make believe names she and her friend, Junko, adopted when their families lived in adjoining apartments in the tenement on lower south side Chicago. She hated her own name. And they would dream together of escape from endless clotheslines, the taunting boys whose haircuts were shaped like bowls. Her mother, the fair skinned, untouchable, "beautiful one" was a shadow to her, who cried in anger when she'd tantrum for attention. Yuki floated in and of her daughter's life with many suitors. The handsome Haru brought flowers until they got married. He would even woo the daughter.

She could understand why any man would court her mother. Yuki seemed created to have a man take care of the delicate, snow like beauty. After their marriage, Haru brought them west to the farm, where her mother worked like a man.

She imagined Yuki was only happy when she was in bed with Haru. She complained a lot otherwise. In the early evening, sometimes she'd see a happy glaze over her mother's eyes. Those times, late at night, she'd be awakened by the suppressed moan, the whispers of Haru: "Yuki, kimochi eh." The tender calm of those moments, hearing the closeness of bodies, she would feel the strange stir in herself, where the thighs met, and she'd be ashamed of the wet and toss herself to sleep.

Yuki would catch Haru staring at the young girl's developing body, fuller busted, elongated, articulate.

When the daughter first bled, frightened, ashamed, Yuki told her it was because she was thinking too much about forbidden things, and she must not let any man kiss her or she would become pregnant. Her schoolmates laughed at her for weeks when she repeated that horror to them.

The perimeters of her being were defined by the growing shape of her flesh. Use it well, she was told and she would know happiness.

When Gerald fondled her, his hands were oppressive, too present, but his eyes were someplace else. Not seeing, but watching as she groaned in the right tone, closed her eyes in feigned ecstacy. He kneaded her breasts as if they could rise, as she heaved herself up. He would bring himself to release and leave her to shower.

She would try to talk to him of Spinoza, Augustine and British law, but it bored her, and he could conduct monologues for hours. "Politics is simply a transient reflection of society's mood . . . frivolous, predictable, shallow. Without immutable law, humans would be reduced to irrational barbarians. War, for example, is a logical manifestation of the irrational nature of man. And for man, all is fair in war." She wished he would hold her again.

The train became a part of her. It breathed for her. Whatever it felt, Yuki felt. The belly of her child, heaving. The belly of the train rancid. California was a dream. A place/ blurred with the smell of vomit, as she had boarded the other train to another desert place.

Sachiko gagging. Sachiko of the ready smile, quick to comfort, sensitive to the others' hurt, making infants laugh with her laughter, lifting even Ojichan from his gloom, with antics commanding joy.

Guardtowers held young men, barely men. Rifled. Helmets hiding their eyes. They were there a long time.

One day, Ojichan went to the barbed fence, looking for pieces of wood to carve, forgetting the forbidden closeness to the gate. When he stooped to grasp the wood, the boy in the tower abruptly drew his rifle. Yuki gasped. Sachiko suddenly slid to him, laughter loud. Pulled him from the fence. "you will make me a fine Daruma from that." Ojichan, smiling, not noticing the soldier's frightened aim, led back to life by Sachiko. Yuki wanted to cry like an infant, her own in her arms, squirming for her breastmilk.

Immutable law . . ." the consequences of law are unquestionable. Debateable, but unquestionable," Gerald droned. "one can question the morality of warfare, especially nuclear, but one cannot deny that the dropping of the A-bomb in Japan ended the war unconditionally . . . they surrendered. And isn't that the bottom line ? to win, regardless."

"They had made peace overtures before the bomb was dropped, I read . . ." she interjected. "But war doesn't justify any country being used as America's laboratory . . ."

"Atrocity is inconsequential. People forget," he huffed. "My Lai is also called an atrocity, but in the context of the situation, is a means to an end. Besides, in World War II, we would have had to share the spoils of war with Russian if we didn't drop . . ." His face swelled with a smile.

"The spoils of war . . ." she began to weep.

"You're too emotional. Each event has a matching mark in history . . . there is nothing new under the sun . . ."

Then there is no hope for me, she thought.

Words like a wall, keeping her out, locking her in. Words choking her in the face of something so wrong. Empty space between the space of letters in her head. Win. Profit. Human life inconsequential. They would not surrender. All is fair in war . . . Do the people know what the generals weave ?

Gerald ceased fire for the night. Lifting her to the demilitarized zone. Pulled the bedcover. She, drowning in a wave of sheets, surrendering to dark sleep :

The road shimmered across farmlands in the heat.

Three families managed the farms, and expanded little by litte, though they were poor and had to start over on their land after the war.

Everyone was irritable today because of the heat wave, unrelenting, windless.

All the children wanted to play across the road where the creek ran, the cool relief of that shaded place, willows hanging like they'd been there forever. Even they drooped more.

The children loved to catch tadpoles in the spring, and in the heavy summer months, when the frogs were everywhere, they caught them in jars, fed them dragonflies.

The water was a magic place where fantasies became real. The stream carrying her to the sea, where she played like a mermaid, singing in the sun, traveling continents, speaking strange tongues, scaling new mountains, plunging new depths, dancing in the holiness of music.

Today, with the heat stabbing their skin, the children begged to go to their creek. Her cousin, dark eyed, blossom lipped Sachiko, thin, quick, short straight bangs whipping as she ran, was scolded for her impatience. She was older, about 14, and always leading the others, laughing as she danced with the pebbles on the path to the creek.

The road was a freeway to another large town, and traffic was always too fast. They were cautioned frequently.

Sachiko broke from the younger cousins, eager to get to the cool shade. The screaming of brakes pierced the dense heat. Everyone ran, suddenly chilled, hoping it was a chicken, a dog or another small animal they often saw split by the tires of speeding cars. The children were stopped near the open gate to the road. All the adults ran down the road quite a ways where the car had veered crazily and stopped.

Afterward, Yuki, tears choking, told them Sachiko had been thrown so far it took them a few minutes to find her. Her thin legs, like the stalks of grass jutting from the ground on the side of the road.

"We should have taken it." Haru almost shouted.

Startled, Yuki looked up slowly, her red eyes burning with more than grief. "$200.00?" she almost hissed. "We'll see," Haru said. "We'll see what the courts do for a hakujin and what they do for us." His jaw was working tightly, as he jarred out of the room.

She thought she would suffocate in the room full with the women's sobs, their grief shrouding the walls. Death was a stranger to her then. .

She sat up in the darkness. Gerald grunted softly and stirred, turned on his side. Her skin prickled as she felt the terrible emptiness of air on her arms. "Without the law, humans would be reduced . . ."

Attorney Magnusen said they should not sue. Costly, lengthy for an accident. Settle out of court.

Incense circling over Sachiko's coffin. Silent lines of mourners. Chants and white paper over flowers. She was held as they viewed the body. Sachiko looked older lying there. She reached out a hand to stroke the pale cheek. Suddenly she was very afraid.

The family got nothing from the man who said he was not drunk when his car hit the kid. She came from nowhere he had said, like a chicken flying across the road.

Law, mutable by the makers.

The days of her life flew on. She was panicking because she would soon finish her degree. Somehow she couldn't face the end of this phase of her life. The institution kept her snug in its rigidity, its walls promising to keep everything the same until she could find the strength to move on, tomorrow. There were practical problems like money. And she was bored with the menial jobs. Maybe she could use the sociology. Gerald encouraged her to get a Ph.D. The relationship certainly had no feeling of progression, but it was one she would rather kill than break or change.

The world he wanted to keep her in was sufficiently isolated and protective of his values that she would continue to receive the same realities . . . brick on brick, the tomb was still attractive.

She went for an interview for a part-time summer position at the Community Counseling Service. The black man who sat behind his disarrayed desk was muscular, animated, his flesh shining as he talked and smiled. She was aware of the look he gave her as their conversation coursed through many subjects, and she wanted to draw closer. When he asked her to dinner, she lowered her eyes, a technique she had learned. Busy tonight or anytime? Wanting to keep him near, but not too near, she looked at her hands.

His eyes flashed, and her blood sang with fear, excitement, dread. It depends . . . she started.

"On whether you get this job or not?" he interrupted. Her mouth was open, caught. "You intellectual broads are all the same. Same game, same line, same pose."

The sinking feeling of losing herself again . . . it had something to do with guilt.

Her uncle offered her a walk through the field. It was dark. She had stayed at her grandmother's too long. She welcomed the offer. In the hot night, toads were thick on the dust dry stretch where the corn had been cut. She dreaded stepping on them. Obscene croaks. He held the flashlight so she could see the toads parting the path, his free arm on her shoulders. Flashlight clicked off. The ground silently leaping around her. Thoughts of escape. No courage to step through the toads. Nervous laugh. Feeble shove. Darkness like toads, swallows wandering insects.

After bathing, she approached Yuki, still shaken and asked why her uncle would want to touch her in that way. Her mother rose up with a surprising rage . . . "What did you do . . ." "he wouldn't do that unless . . ." Her young body quivered in a strange abstract guilt, not understanding but certain her mother spoke with a knowledge that came from some experience of her own. Blushing, she tried to protest, but her mother was lost to her. Her rage turned cold, as the child shivered in the wake of accusations.

Woman. victim ? violator ? perpetrator ? The conspiracy.

"Don't you have it turned around," she began to protest.

His face grew darker : "you use your body like your mind. A lot of pages of books that you can quote, memorized. You can't even field a hit. You probably have some steps you've memorized for a *meaningful relationship*, so you don't have to fuck. really fuck. You have *intercourse*. All up there. You won't cop to your responsbility . . ."

"Who do you think . . ."

"You come in here for a job, lead the game, spout sociological garbage and pretend it ain't happening." His eyes burned with an anger she knew nothing about. It frightened her. But she couldn't leave. Something made her stay, and they talked. They talked.

He stood up, over her, pulled her up from her chair, gently, and held her for some moments.

Fingers burning. Flesh searing. His warmth reaching. He was honest and it touched a deep need she did not know she had. Her life built on mistrust and fear. His directness attracting/repelling her. She felt herself fade again, not able to keep her presence in his embrace. The flame he built in her she washed with denial. When he pulled her face to his, she turned away, the old vacuum creeping into her belly.

Suddenly, he pulled her hair back. Whispered protests. Small fists whipping, pushing. He humped over her, containing movement. His mouth opened. Loud laugh. He fully clothed. Laughing as he released her, she struggled with the clothing, choking crimson, weak with humiliation. He was still laughing . . . "Better go Home . . ." as she vanished.

Yuki, Haru stood like flames before the yawning black square of Sachiko's grave. They flickered in the sunset, shoulders firm as if to hold back final statements. She stood between them, feeling their pillar strength. She quieted at Haru's iron set face.

Going home from the cemetary, Haru spoke gently to Yuki, "Sorry I asked you to take the money." That was one of the few times she ever heard "sorry" from him.

"We'll fight, Yuki. Magnusen isn't the only attorney around. Too bad Yas isn't in California. He'd show that judge something." Uncle Yas, Haru's brother who finished first in law school and practicing in Chicago.

His voice rose in controlled fury, addressing something beyond Yuki. "We can't give up. Too much too long."

Yuki was sobbing, wet words streaming . . . "How much suffering."

"What good does that do ? Suffering forever. What matters is how you bear it when it happens. We won't be broken. Besides. It never stopped when we were quiet."

She had not hear such a clear, focused fire. The car seared the road, spinning through Haru's hurt, crushing the brush that blew across his path. She knew she mustn't speak. It is that pride when violated that flares and threatens everything around it. And she thrilled in the beauty of its strength.

They fought. The new lawyer was indifferent, they said, and he didn't push for anything. But they fought. Each day, Haru would wear a tie, he hated, and his best jacket ; Yuki would put on her suit, and they'd go with Sachiko's parents to the court. Each day, they returned. Drained, firm lipped. Haru holding all of them tightly in his determination.

She would catch Yuki looking at him, her face open, admiring. Yuki new he was set to get what he wanted. Even though their weariness told them the case was lost, she felt Haru steadily fight even those who had given up, to win the suit against the man he called murderer.

Case dismissed.

Haru spoke no more of it. But hurt glistened from him like a tree wearing rain.

Don't forget from where you have come. Don't desert dignity to endure. Don't abandon the struggle to shape your own soul.

The sound of his laugh burning in her being. Something she knew she did. The collusion with the game. And she was left faceless. He had stripped her of even her body . . . the only means of her definition. He exposed, lay bare, revealed fully, and finally rejected the empty shell. The deceptions upon which she had built her life.

Refusal to take responsibility. Making herself victim was the punishment. Self fulfilling destruction. She walked for a long time into the evening not knowing the direction.

> *Visions of famine*
> *like trees*
> *burned from a fist of flame*
> *I wander from village*
> *to village*
> *asking stalks of people*
> *who stare with eyes*
> *hollow from too much light.*
> *Where is home ?*
> *Silence follows me*
> *like the clouds.*

*Answer please.*
*The ground rises*
*with a terrible swell*
*of smells from bodies*
*buried in her.*

She found herself by the beach. The water thundering in her. The rage of foam spat on her face as she thought again, again, of the man today, the erection on her chest as she lay on the floor, pinned like an insect who had come too close to the flame.

| | |
|---|---|
| *Arashi* | *Storm wind* |
| *fuku* | *blows* |
| | *ocean waves outstretched* |
| | *clutching for the moon.* |

Her mind tossed, something in her ribs searing. Foam like fingers reaching for her thighs. Seaweed spread like strands of a dying woman. Flame growing. She had not cried like this before. Water streaming from her shoulders.

| | |
|---|---|
| *Ame* | *Rain    Rain* |
| *Ame furu* | *dressing the flame* |
| | *in strands of* |
| | *silver* |

She shivered and ran to the rain cleaned streelights. She wanted to curl up in the safe, predictable placeof Gerald's weight. At least it was something she could touch . . . turmoil follows, everywhere.

That night, as he held her in the foam of sheets, t.v. blasting, she looked into the mouth of night and saw the electronic vision clearly before her. Between gasps of the fucking. T.V. droning

Nixon, nose skiing to the corners of his jaws, fingering long stems of microphones, pumping with fists for emphasis . . . "it is necessary to escalate penetration into enemy harbors. These communists stop at nothing . . . spread like maggots in a democracy clean world . . ."

She longed to draw him closer, closer . . . as if driven to experience the depths of torture. She cast away her own body, plummeting the emptiness, scaling the strange new pain.

"of course Lt. Calley was acting in the line of duty. . . . necessary to show we mean business."

Gerald stroking her flesh.

"napalm is a success . . . their surrender imminent . . ."

mounting her again, pressing breath from her.

"my fellow americans . . . the spoils of war . . ."

as he entered / grinding deep within her

"we'll bomb them to the peace table . . ."

releasing without thought to her reaching

electronic eyes following the pumping bodies, sweat popping,
"victory at all cost . . ."

The sick feeling spread to her arms, as she clawed his shoulder to dismount.
This was not desire. Her shape changed / defined by the slit she needed filled.
filled.

> *Umi     Ocean*
> *Kagami  mirror of the night*
> *          show me nothing.*
> *          Everything.*

Gerald took her to a dinner party given by friends. "very influential with
the bar association." chic, glib, society's elite. Stiff discomfort for her. Gerald
smiling a lot. Indifferent conversations on war, politicians, My lai, cuisine.
Voices raised in consternation, intense, angry voices on the injustice toward
ducks . . . victims of oil. Angry indignation about whales and jap whalers.

> *Kujira   whales sounding*
> *ochite    where did the fish hide*
> *          when the water*
> *          filled with death's light*

They say the worst way to go is by drowning. Slow. Except for unforeseen
attacks, where weeks, years after the mushroom cloud people vomited up
their life.
     She remembered the helpless flock of chickens, scattered by the slightest
sound. Her heart felt like that, flying across the road in the path of crushing
tires. Not able to take flight, splattered on dead asphalt.
     The scavengers feasted.

> *1941 newsflashes. Boycott Japan. "The question was how*
> *we should maneuver Japan into firing the first shot without*
> *allowing too much danger to ourselves . . . we have provoked*
> *war . . ." stated the secretary of war.*

Flame in her fueling. All is fair in war. flame rising. bone burning.
Mushroom clouds flashing.

"We do live from the ocean," laughed Mr. Hashimoto. His
gentle laugh warming his customers when he came with his

truck. All the Japanese American farmers called it the "ark" because it connected them to each other. He delivered foodstuffs from Japan they couldn't buy anywhere in the predominantly white nearby towns.

Octopus, dried shrimp, kamabuko, unagi, real rice, fresh tofu – everything they craved for their diets. The women, all the children, even sometimes Haru, would run out to greet Hashimoto-san, rejoicing in his Wednesday visits.

They would not only get their essential food supplies, but the latest news about the Yamaguchi's new baby, the crop failure of the Shimizu's, the illness of Mrs. Arai, the big catch of trout by Mr. Asaki. Mr. Hashimoto would be an hour or so late sometimes because he would be so busy conveying good wishes, get wells, and good lucks exchanged between the farmer families in the vast area he covered with his truck.

Yuki said, "He's such a good man," when they couldn't pay up their bills some weeks, and he would cheerfully whisper, "next time."

When Hashimoto-san became ill, his color paled, his smile dimmed. They would give him gifts, home remedies, tell him to slow down. Still he came every week, knowing they could not get their food from home . . .

She thought she would never forget Mr. Hashimoto's smile, and the fish smells from his wonderful ark.

Provoke war, tramping to the rhythm of her footsteps. The scattered plates of food thrown at the shocked dinner party still sticking on her shoes. She couldn't remember the words spuming from her at the doughfaced gathering, but she knew she wouldn't be seeing him / them again.

> *Action is the name*
> *for hope.*

She had walked very far. The street lights in the fog were an eery runway. dangerous for flight. ready for flight. Her face burned into shape. Her nameless face tingling in the fog, mixed with salt.

> *Gold flesh shouts*
> *remember me.*
> *Colors were so vivid*
> *in her other eye.*
> *Crimson walls and live*
> *flowers jumping from*
> *her mother's throat*
> *barbed wire crowning her hair.*

*Little by little*
*she remembers the shadow*
*of herself*
*dancing in the presence*
*of flowers,*
*grandmother,*
*and the language of the sea.*
*Yuki, nodding,*
*as blood*
*flows from her forehead*
*waving goodbye,*
*my nameless child.*
*Wear live flowers*
*in your hair – you will die.*
*Live again*
*in a new time*
*and send me*
*back yourself.*

The cold, like the hate she felt for herself, retreated from her blood. Pumping another song. She wished she could talk to Haru, just once, and let him know what she let herself remember.

She called Haru, "Papa." Always came in after dark from the work . . . his weariness like a coat he slowly shed as Yuki brought him hot tea. He had beautiful arms, lean, taut. Long arms that lifted heavy sacks of grain. She thought he must be very strong, because he carried them without straining, carefully, like a body.

Those sacks of grain. Like gold. No. food for life. She would have to go to the stockroom, and sweep up any that had spilled, carefully like coins. No. food for life.

The man with the red, beefy face, with the stomach shaped like a pear, would come every week to collect the bill for the grain. He'd stand around, eyes shifting at Yuki's behind, until Papa came out ; then he'd laugh, holding out his hand.

Papa never shook his hand. She never told him how proud that made her.

She had heard that when a child is about to be born, the family hangs blue fish to insure the birth of sons. She wondered how blue the fish before her birth.

*Water reaching*
*foam spraying*
*the shape of men*
*of our race/emerging*
*without fins.*
*Where have you been?*
*Looking to a faceless mirror*
*I have hated you*
*father, turning away from me.*
*My need for your love*
*so deep*
*you, out of reach*
*like this sea*
*that circles the world*
*to the place that is home.*
*Gold skinned men*
*firm lipped men*
*black eyed, silent*
*men – touch me.*
*Turning, turning*
*from myself*
*i could not see you –*
*dust covered hands*
*pain wracked pride*
*sweat tracked backs*
*muscles popping from the weight.*
*Dignity is to be unbroken*
*i did not hear your strength unspoken.*
*Love deep/hurt deeper,*
*we destroy*
*before we change.*
*Love spreads like the shoreline*
*crumbles everything*
*even the great rocks*
*of hate we sculpt.*

Wave on wave, the ocean stretched for her, linking her to a place she would slowly remember . . . "better go home . . ."

Home was changed. new. Yuki, Haru standing like strong trees in a yellow sunrise.

She, no longer faceless. Barefaced. The ocean raged, but she was not the helpless vessel tossed. She was the foam

*the ocean's hem*
*dancing in the sanctity*
*of its sound,*
*circling full*
*around.*

In the deep cave of night she called, contrapuntal to the water's cry, My Name is Hatsuko.

*Never be faceless*
*and silent*
*when you are near*
*the shore that*
*is your own strange song.*

## A Song for You

for Cecil


You laugh
your big laugh
your hands
        like wings
        or a dancer's wish
enclosures for the last / first sleep

I want to
hold
suck
taste your skin
breathing in
that dark, deep

I want to
bathe your limbs
like trees
your roots
entangled hard in mine

and walk your back
from Tokyo
to Dar Es Salaam
lulling you with genmai tea

touch me
sing me
make me born
together we will
sound lost bones
and color their flesh

yes,
we will hold
the sea
you and i
and bring
the deep / moist / soft
mouth
to the shores
of all
our continents.

## Lullabye

My mother merely shakes
her head
when we talk about the war,
the camps,
the bombs.

She won't discuss
the dying / her own
as she left her self
with the stored belongings.

She wrapped her shell
in kimono sleeves
and stamped it third class
delivery to Tule Lake

> *futokoro no ko*
> > *child at my breast*
> *oya no nai*
> > *parentless*

What does it mean to be citizen ?

> *It is privilege*
> *to pack only what you can carry*

> *It is dignity*
> *to be interned for your own good*

> *It is peace of mind*
> *constituted by inalienable right*

She x'd the box mark "other"

pledging allegiance
to those who would have turned
on the gas mercifully

*Her song :*
*shikata ga nai*
            *it can't be helped*

She rode on the train
destined for ommission
with an older cousin

who died next to her
gagging when her stomach burned out.

Who says you only die once ?

            *My song :*

            *Watashi ga kadomo wa matte eru*
            *I am a child waiting*
                        *waiting*

            *Watashi no hahaga umareta*
                *for the birth of my mother.*

## The Fisherman

Ojichan was a fisherman/farmer
more a fisherman,
cleaning his bait
winding his line,
the smell of sardines
seeping from his sea-cracked hands.
The muscles of his face spoke
but his tongue silent
except for syllables
of survival
>              sake
>              oi ocha
>              kata o momu
and obachan would
knead the strong knots
on his shoulders.
Only when he put on his boots
and left the house for China Lake
pipe cocked in his mouth
a certain way,
there seemed a light
from his straightened frame
eyes noisy,
muscles in a little dance.
And when he came home,
laughing as he fished his catch
from the depths of his box,
gloated that his old friend
Kinjo caught only one,
and set the stiff rainbow
pearled fish
out for the women to scale,
wide mouths gaping
surprised eyes encorpsing
the room.
Many nights
over sake
making guttural sounds
with Kinjo,
the light from him was brighter.

That winter
China Lake was
cold. winds shaped water
into hands, fingers
clawed the shore
No one else would go
but Kinjo
rocking years and pride
rowed out with his son.
The boat turned
like a small fish
The old man
went down
water freezing in his bones.
His son reached for him,
dived two times
did not come up again.
The people
stood on the dock
and looked.
        I think it hurt Ojichan
deeply
Kinjo fished from China Lake.
        After,
he would sit
looking into the sun,
body dimmed
muscles knotted
eyes silent.
He wore his loss like his heavy boots,
legs moving
in slow underwater motion
when he learned how they
stood and looked
and did nothing.

## Attack the Water

Juxtaposition of war photos
and news flashes, 1942/1972

My first flash
on the newsprint/face
she could have been
Obachan
back then/just after
the camps
when the land/dried/up

no water for months.

In town,
they would not sell
to japs.

We had to eat what
we could grow
that's only natural.

We ate rice with roots.

Vietnamese woman
her face etched old
by newsprint/war
mother/grandmother
she has beared them all

(have they all died ?)

Flash ! !
"they are bombing the waterways . . .

"this new offensive
which has previously/been/avoided/
for//humanitarian//reasons/
will/seriously/jeopardize
their//food//situation ! !"

Obachan
sitting
breathing heavily
in the sun
watching her pet rabbits
(she loved them like children)

which one

tonight ?

I still remember her eyes
drawing the blood
like water.

And the rice –
there were maggots
in the rice.

no water
to flush/them/out.

                    Up river
                    bodies floated in My Chanh
                    eyes eaten by crabs
                    flushed onto the land –

                    fly food.

                    *"They/are/ attacking the water/*
                    *when all else fails*
                    *Attack the Water."*

Obachan
would chew
the food first/ spit
out maggots.

Grandchildren
ate
the spit-flushed rice.

        When all else fails
        attack the water.

## When She Enters

for D . . .

When she sings
with her eyes, the room
dances and her earrings loop
trances around the moon of her face.
Brown skinned / jade fingers
cymbals on her tongue.
And all the brothers
are captured
in the fine flare of her nostrils
She sways,
whispers
i love you
to each in the silent
breathing of her hems
And everyone
wants
to make her their own
even just for the night.
It is like
holding your own cheetah
gazelle with a lion's soul
pacing that sensual pace
when encaged.
Feel the secret power
to contain
the wild pacing / you
can't tame.
She will kill you
if she can
any second now
escape / maul / enflame
but you love the
pain
even more
knowing you can't keep her.

# Drowning in the Yellow River

Necking in back seats

of convertibles with white boys
while elvis
creams out your pain

> screams out your song
> "you ain't nothin' but a . . ."

who else am i ?

The silk scarf obachan
gave you
you wear like ann margaret
in convertible winds

> flapping to
> "don't step on my . . ."

who else am i ?

look at me —
buddaheads
chinamen who stand
on one side of the room
and don't mess with girls

who else am i ?

necking is so hard
in the back seat
with white boys
had to pee so bad
crossing your legs

> elvis panting
> "don't be cruel"

she couldn't say
stop suckin' on my neck daddy-o
gotta go
to the obenjo

> one once asked if jap toilets
> had horizontal plumbing

who else am i ?

crossing your legs
slid the silk scarf
into your crotch

                    elvis stops for a commercial
                  "wonder where the yellow went . . ."

obachan's silk scarf
sucked the yellow river
you came home
rumpled
hickied

(he'll call you again sometime)

you hung
your yellowed
pee-drowned scarf to dry

who else am i ?

# Breathe Between the Rain

For Bayani & Serafin, poets
who live among us still.

We, gathered in this place
stars like eyes
watching our words
How many in our numbers ?

> We lost Bayani
> that day
> his soul flying
> before him
> eager to fathom the light
> flesh twitching
> from a spirit's kiss
> He saw too deep
> to stay among us.

and

> Serafin
> pain bundled
> between his eyes
> bursting through his veins
> like his love
> he left us
> with an ache
> that would last forever
> and visions of manongs
> as beautiful as carabao
> lifting their necks
> to the wind.

Count our numbers.
Don't mourn losses too long
or it will render us useless
like vessels emptied.
Listen instead to the song
their legacy of strength.
We can circle our own
ritual,
make language,
new words, rooted in our bones.

A dance
to bear us to safety
muscling strong.
Listen to their song
rhyming with survival
teach our children
that nothing is more precious
than human life.
Count our numbers.

      We lost Minoru
      when they came to take us
      died of shame
      in Topaz
      died of shame

know our true enemy.

      We lost Shigemi
      hiding in the tall stems
      of yellow flowers
      they even shot
      off the heads of chrysanthemums

Count our numbers.
harvest our strength.
breathe between the rain.
We shall not go into their camps again.

The dirt beneath the graves will speak
From between our thighs will come new tribes.

## September Second

On the Victory of the People of
Vietnam. To Mrs. Huong

It is the second of September
the leaves are turning
red tinges the edges
like fingers dripping.
There has been much blood
sucked by our mother
the earth
she has received your children.
I will not forget your face
as you spoke of them
interning them in our minds
describing their lovely eyes
as the cages bled their life.
Each day / as the sun mourned,
the crazy fire
dropped by the enemy
branded their infamy.
It is the second of September
I hope you are well
the sun warming your face
as you visit your children's graves
your hands rebuilding the earth
the sun will repair
one day.

You, i remember
as you have been burned in my listening body
I long to hear you
speak of this day
the earth rejoicing
with the sound of your songs
It is the second of September
and the wind
touching the arms
of trees
leaves / bleeding
we will not forget
your many children / Vietnam.

It is the second of September
and the wind is marching
blowing the leaves like banners
singing through our bodies
clothing the earth like a spirit
marching
victorious
I am with you
my sister
and my tears
wash gladly
as I see you / glimmering
alive / free.

## A Lecherous Poem to Toshiro Mifune

The sound of
shakuhachi
is oozing around my mind.
Beautiful
samurai / rebel
squared in the snow
with eye-blinking speed
sliced the wind
and opponent,
blood bursting the cold air.
His woman is looking on
in the high field
breasts heaving
obi flying
He squares his back
arms hidden
shoulders keeping time
to his leaving
her behind.
Toshiro, you don't ever get down
with your women
why don't you ?
I can really get into you
sitting in that room alone,
sifting the thoughts of your
ancients,
mind and body
one with your sword
but
must you scorn her
all the time ?
Don't misunderstand –
I really dig
that ritual –
that clear, clean
blade of discipline,
that taut wire
connected with my ancestors,
that gathering of all time
into moment beyond all time
that put / feeling / aside
one / ness / with / nature / self

perfectly in tune
        like the
               "bell ringing in an empty sky"

like the

        flute crying alone

like the

        sound of sun on stone.

And oh, Mifune,
you are so fine
I can sit with you for hours
and wait
and wait
for that climax
for that instant whipping of your blade

ckhhhhhhhaaaap !

but as you walk off
in the wind blown lonely
twilight,
without even looking back
your high
wide
stepping in time
to japanese / cowboy music,

i am
that woman
kimono clad
silent and motionless
(except for heaving breast)
suppressing all the frustation / emptiness
not wanting that loneliness

i am
that hair tearing
hara-kiri prone /
longing / licking
body-burning-for-you
woman of the dunes.

Turn around Mifune ! !

stop cleaning your blade.

we can make

an eternity

together.

## The Question Is

Yellow is
the color of lemons,
sun,
early morning on water.

I, with other thoughts,
encounter you –
your blue eyes
dissolving with doubtful words of love,
whispering to me :

> You are so
> exotic
> so curiously pale
>
> Your Kind
> has always attracted me
>
> Your slanted eyes
> hold mysteries of the orient
>
> Give me
> your novelty body.
>
> But before you do
> the Question
> Is
> it true
> your cunt is slanted too ?

## Crazy Alice

Aunt Alice, who has touched the sun . . .
victim of American Concentration Camps

She came to the
wedding
in a tattered coat
called us all by
the wrong names

Yukio / Mizume / Kyoko

No, crazy Alice
We died in the camps

          remembering / remembering
          Alice / back then

and the relatives
laughed behind
her back / crazy Alice

          the bride is beautiful
          who is she ?

crazy Alice
it is your daughter

          *okashi ne*
          *jinsei wa okashi*

          life's so strange
          before the war
          i had a name

twenty years ago
she would come to us
face blue
eyes like black walnuts
and down her nose
blood flowed like tears

battered by husbands
and lovers
for hoarding food
and love

where has love gone ?

the children
will starve
remember the war
eating potato roots


and thinking of
invasions
and prison camps
she opened her legs
to the white boss man


*okashi ne*
*jinsei wa okashi*

life's so strange
before the war
i had a name


crazy Alice
where do you wander ?
you walk on the sun
your eyes
keep the years
motionless
and your tears like rain
on a sleeping sea

my child is hungry
what will i do


crazy Alice
    crazy Alice

she is the bride
standing before you

my child is dead
my breasts dried
during the war
and she died
from hunger


rejoice
Crazy Alice / your child
has a new name

*okashi ne, okashi*
*Jinsei wa okashi*

life's so strange
before the war
i was my child
i had a name.

## Canto a Neruda

"I among men bear the same wounded hand
suffer the same reddened cup
and live an identical rage."

Pablo Neruda

Mountains are
crying
in shame

Rivers are outraged

Cities crumble
from the people's
pain

       This was Vietnam
       Chile's anguish
       Mindanao

       Blood crosses oceans
       floods the streets.

Flesh tightened on bones
Flesh washed by blood
Flesh gutted by flies.

With so many friends already
dead
and others who will die
ripped by war

will they tell us
how ravenous the worms
crawling beneath
our living skin ?

will we listen ?

       How many my lais
       atticas
       santiagos
       will bloat our brains
       in silent rage ?

many of our friends
are dead
will they tell us of the worms
invading our bones ?

We awake to weep,
Allende

They are burning
the breasts of our mother
the earth.

Your sleep within her restless.

And Neruda,
Does that wound in your heart
still hurt ?

They fear your words
They burn your words
But your spirit is afire in us.

In our bodies
a terrible thunder
is building its nest.

## Hospitals Are To Die In

They finally
had to take obachan
she was dying

      hospitals
      takai
          takai
      she whispered

but she is dying

when they carried her
body
barely breathing,
they were carrying my soul
wrapped in the thin sheath
of her skin.

The ambulance attendants
rushed from their
coffee break
irritated,
dropped her on the
stretcher
and bumped her
against the door
violating her sleep

She wanted to stay
die in the house
that was like a body
wrapping her
in smells she knew
breathing memories
for her.

In the corners
of her closed eyes
silent tears brimming
protesting
not the hospital

      cold
      white
      expensive

the attendants swore
as they slung
the stretcher

complaining
about the high cost of living.

One said
he had to buy a
side of beef
to hang in his freezer.

        it's cheaper that way.

## Awake in the River

The desert place. The child knew no other home.

The tortoise crawls in the hot sun. The special sun, like imprisoned, never seeming to move over the flat, flat land. Darkness falls suddenly like a velvet cloth. With it the cold, when the tortoise sleeps.

The child ran barefoot all the time, digging her toes deep into the sand, like a clawed reptile. Unlike them, she could not go beyond the barbed wire.

> Sleep,
> her mother sang,
> the sun will sap
> blood through your pores
> and make you weak.
> Sleep
> in the desert.

When the soldiers came each day, jaws like iron, picking up the men to take them to distant potato fields, she would run after her grandfather, sitting in the back of the army truck with the others, silent. Teeth gripped. Swallowing rage. Her small legs barely would reach the gate as the truck disappeared through the dust.

> Rebellion
> waits outside the gate,
> slowly gathering
> like sounds of angry snowgeese
> or water from the mountain
> springing free.
> Ocean's throat
> calls the awakening.

The children found the tortoise, big, dull shelled, making a slow journey through the desert. They named it Muhon-nin because it would not retreat into its shell, put it in the garden the men had grown from stones and succulents. Making beauty from adversity.

Old men would carve from dead wood in the shade of barracks, resurrecting images of fierce gods. Women made feasts from rations to feed strength. Weaving songs with hidden messages.

> Nenneko, nenneko ya      sleep, little one
> nashite naku yara        why do you cry ?

Let the tortoise go, the women would say. It is wrong to imprison any living thing.

| Kodomo ga | children |
|---|---|
| nemutte iru | sleeping |
| | frozen time |
| | entombs the race |
| | when will we wake ? |

The child, always digging, stepped deep onto a nail. Blood pouring from the bottom of her body. Mother in fear, whispering . . . For those who do not feign sleep, a strange life will follow. Turmoil threatens. Freedom's still a distant harvest.

The tortoise escaped. The children wept.

| Kame kame | Tortoise takes |
|---|---|
| nigeru wa | each step |
| | inevitable as time |
| | full with spawn, |
| | a new age |
| | to the shore |
| | where it will bury eggs. |

Her mother washed her feet each day. The child slept, knowing she would run under another sky.

Born in the desert
cord knotted to woman / belly
by barbed wire.
Womb blazing
Beyond bondage.
The sun spreads
in the sand
touching the lip
of the sea,
rising.

The men kept their war inside. Pulling weeds by roots. Figures bent, not broken, wind rounding their backs. Grandfather wears his wait like a shell. Sleep in the desert, he warned.

Tortoise, empty,
worn,
plunges to the deep.
In the steady
pounding of the waves,
offsprings wake.

Mother steady singing by the crib.

Sleep in the desert.
Awake in the river.

# Afterword

From the eye of racist relocation fever which came about and plagued America during World War II, Janice Mirikitani grew/bloomed/fought as a desert flower behind barbed wire. She grew with that pain, of what it all represented ; from the multinational corporations to war from Korea to Vietnam to Latin America to Africa to Hunter's Point and Chinatown. *Awake in the River* screams those memoirs, the lessons and a prophesy as only one from within the cage of the American nightmare would know.

Janice Mirikitani, a sansei, lives and works in San Francisco. She has been published in numerous anthologies and textbooks. She has also co-edited several anthologies. Janice has organized and participated in many community projects and programs. She is currently serving as the project director of the Japanese American Anthology Project. Her works have appeared in *Third World Women, Time to Greez, AION* magazine and more. In her words :

> Words from the Third World, like food,
> fortifying the act, universal, essential,
> procreative, freeing, connective, satisfying.

*George Leong*
Editor
Isthmus Press

Partially funded by a grant from the NEA (a federal agency)

Isthmus Press
Box 6877
San Francisco, CA 94101

Typeset by John McBride
& printed by Braun-Brumfield